Rockschool Po 8070 £15.99

D0247073

Better Vocals With

Rockschool

A *Rockschool* Publication
www.rockschool.co.uk

Welcome To Level 1 *Female Vocals*

Welcome to the Rockschool Level 1 candidate pack for Female Vocals. This pack includes all the prepared elements needed by a candidate to take grades 1, 2 and 3. In the book you will find exam scores for the performance pieces consisting of a vocal line and chord boxes.

The CDs have backing tracks for the technical exercises; five of the songs in each grade have two backing tracks in different keys. Examples of all the other tests contained in the exam can be found in the *Companion Guide* accompanying this series.

If you have any queries about this or any other Rockschool exam, please call us on **020 8332 6303** or email us at office@rockschool.co.uk. Visit our website http://www.rockschool.co.uk. Good luck!

Grade 1

At this grade there will be an emphasis on notes, rhythm and intonation. Pieces will generally be within a limited range and only require a basic control of tone. Pieces will be of a length appropriate for the grade and there will be no requirement for vocal improvisation. The use of a microphone is not mandatory but candidates may use one if they feel it will enhance their performance.

Grade 2

At this grade there will be an emphasis on basic style awareness in the use of tone and solid voice. There may be limited use of head voice. Pieces will be of slightly longer duration with an extended range and the use of intervallic leaps.

Grade 3

At this grade there will be an increasing level of stylistic awareness with employment of suitable technique to a basic level. There will be use of solid voice and a limited requirement for head voice. Pieces will be of a suitable length to demonstrate appropriate technique and concentration with an extended range and occasional use of wide intervals.

How To Use The CDs

The Level 1 book contains two CDs. On these you will find the backing tracks to the exercises and the songs. Candidates should prepare the exercises and the songs using these CDs to perform with in the exam.

For the scales and intervals in grades 1, 2 and 3, the first backing track is in the key of A. You will find alternative keys for the scales at the end of the CD in all keys between B♭ and E around middle C. For the intervals, test 1, there are alternative notes from B♭ to B, and for test 2, there are alternative fifths from B♭ to B. Any of these keys can be used in the exam.

Important Information For Candidates

Candidates may use this syllabus to enter for either a **grade exam** or a **performance certificate** at grades 1, 2 or 3. If you are entering for a **grade exam**, you will need to prepare the following elements. You will perform them in the exam in the order in which they are shown below. Full syllabus requirements can be found in the *Rockschool Vocal Syllabus Guide* which can be downloaded from www.rockschool.co.uk.

Technical exercises (15 marks). You will find four sets of exercises printed for each grade: a rhythm test, a scale test, an interval test and a Phrasing & Dynamics test.

General Musicianship Questions (5 marks). You will be asked four questions immediately after the Phrasing & Dynamics test. These questions will focus on aspects of music notation. One final question will be asked at the end of the exam.

- **Grade 1**. 4 questions on dynamic markings and meanings, note values and time signature. 1 question on meaning of lyrics in 1 song.
- **Grade 2**. 4 questions on the above and pitch names, cresc/decresc, rest values. 1 question on expression and performance of 1 song.
- **Grade 3**. 4 questions on the above and recognition of intervals of 2nd and 3rd between two adjacent notes (candidates will not be required to state major or minor), staccato marks, slurs, pitch names within a bar (ie bar 5, 3rd beat, what is the pitch name of that note?) 1 question on expression and performance of 1 song.

Aural Tests (10 marks). There are two aural tests in each grade. Examples are printed in the Companion Guide. The requirements for each grade are as follows:

- **Grade 1**. You will be given a set of three rhythmic examples that are two bars long each. The examiner will play one of the examples on CD and you will be asked to identify the correct answer from the printed examples. You will then be asked to clap back the rhythm and to continue for two further bars in a simple/repetitive manner.
- **Grade 2**. As for Grade 1 but with more complex rhythmic values.
- **Grade 3**. As for Grade 1 but there will be a two bar melody in the same rhythm. You will be asked to sing back the melody and continue to improvise for a further two bars, returning to the tonic. The second test is a two bar chord sequence repeated over eight bars. The candidate will hear the sequence through once and will be required to improvise a major line on the repeat, paying attention to rhythmic repetition and shape. Please refer to the *Syllabus Guide* for specifications. **This test is continuous**.

Three performance pieces (60 marks). You are not limited solely to the songs printed in this book, or the companion Level 1 volume. You may perform **either** three songs from this book (including one or more from the supplementary list printed for each grade), or you may bring in **one** song not included in these lists to perform in the exam. This may be a hit from the chart or a song of your own composing. Please ensure, though, that you have the appropriate backing track. Please turn to the Guru's Guide on page 55 for the list of supplementary material.

Unaccompanied Piece (10 Marks). In addition, you will be asked to perform either a part of one of the pieces you have performed, or a different song, unaccompanied. You will be asked to sing this after you have performed the second accompanied song you have chosen. Please refer to the *Syllabus Guide* for the variation and improvisation requirements.

If you are entering a **performance certificate**, you will perform **five** songs, of which up to **two** may be from repertoire not included in this book or the companion Level 1 volume.

The Level 1 *Female Vocals* book is a companion to the Level 1 *Male Vocals* book. Candidates are welcome to perform repertoire contained in either book in the exam of equivalent difficulty.

Grade 1 *Technical Exercises*

In this section, the examiner will ask you to perform the four exercises printed below. You do not need to memorise the exercises (and you may use the book in the exam) but the examiner will be looking for the speed and confidence of your response. The examiner will also give you credit for the level of your musicality.

Exercise 1: Rhythm

Disc 1 Track 1

You will be asked to perform the exercise below as written to a backing track accompaniment in the exam. A short sound check will be given.

Exercise 2: Scales

Disc 1 Track 2

You will be asked to perform a major scale in the following rhythms to a backing track accompaniment in the exam. You will be allowed to choose your own starting note between **A-E** which will be played to you before you begin. You will be asked a selection by the examiner and you will perform the exercise *legato* to a sound of your own choosing.

Exercise 3: Intervals

This exercise has two parts - (A) You will be asked to pitch a major third above the notes **I**, **IV** and **V** of the chosen key in the above scale. The examiner will play the note for four beats on a CD and you will be asked to hold the note for four beats.

Disc 1 Track 3

(B) You will be asked to pitch the root note of a perfect fifth chosen from the same notes **I**, **IV** and **V**. The examiner will play the interval for four beats on a CD and you will be asked to hold the note for four beats.

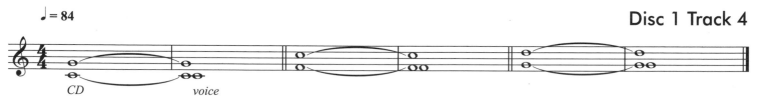

Disc 1 Track 4

Exercise 4: Phrasing & Dynamics   Disc 1 Track 5

You will be asked to prepare the following exercise. The examiner will play the backing on CD and you will be asked to sing the exercise, paying attention to the written phrasing and dynamics. You may perform the exercise using any sound that you consider appropriate.

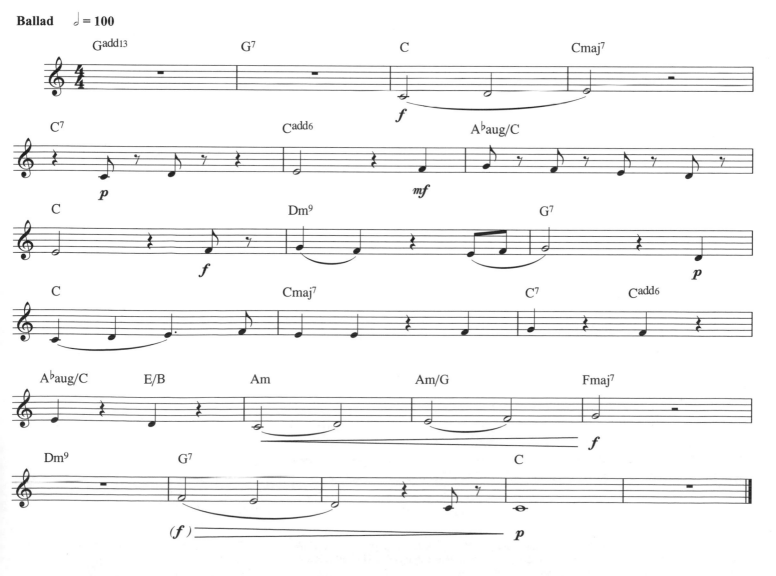

Eternal Flame

Words & Music by Susanna Hoffs,
Tom Kelly & Billy Steinberg

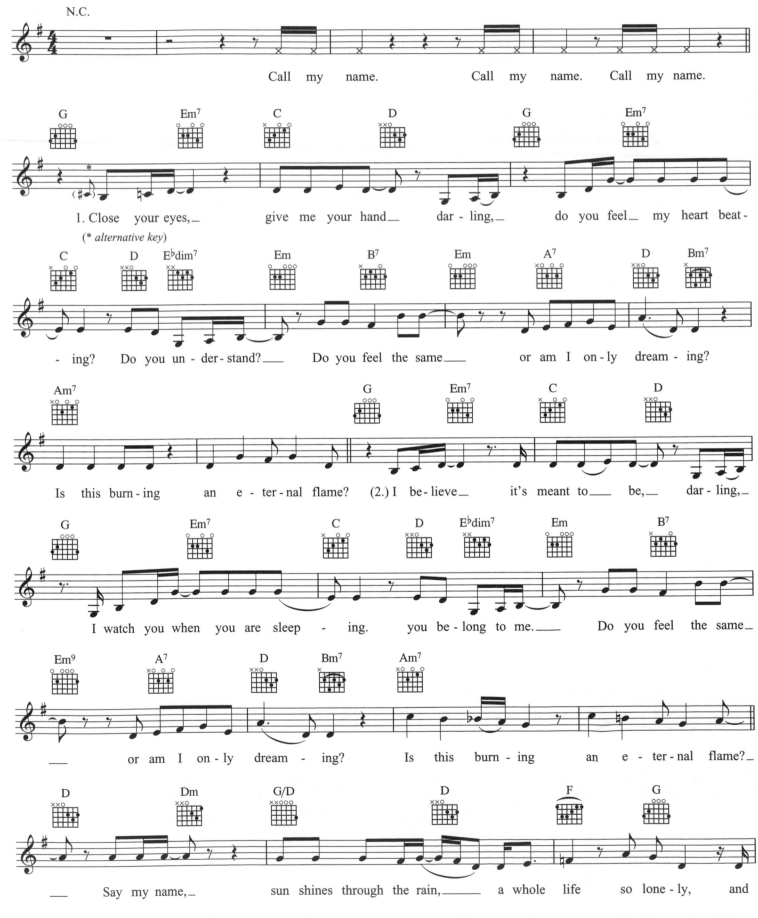

Never Ever

Words & Music by Shaznay Lewis,
Esmail Jazayeri & Sean Mather

♩ = 72 (♫ = ♪³♪)

D♭5   **D♭7**   **G♭**

Spoken: A few questions that I need to know: how could you ever hurt me so?   I need to know what I've done wrong,

D♭   **D♭7**

and how long it's been going on.   Was it that I never paid enough attention,   or did I not give enough affection?

A♭   **A♭9**   **A♭7**   **D♭**

Not only will your answers keep me sane, but I'll   know never to make the same mistake again.   You can tell me to my face,

D♭7   **G♭**   **D♭**

or even on the phone;   you can write it in a letter.   Either way, I have to know.   Did I never treat you right?

A♭   **G♭**   **D♭/F**   **E♭m7**   **D♭**

Did I always start the fight?   Either way I'm going out of my mind.   All the answers to my questions I have to find.

D♭   **D♭7**   **D♭9**   **G♭**

1. My head's spin - ning,   and I am in a daze;___   I feel i - so - la - ted,

(Verse 2 see block lyric)

D♭

I don't want to com - mu - ni - cate.   I'll take a show - er, I will___ scour,

Vocals Level 1 - Female

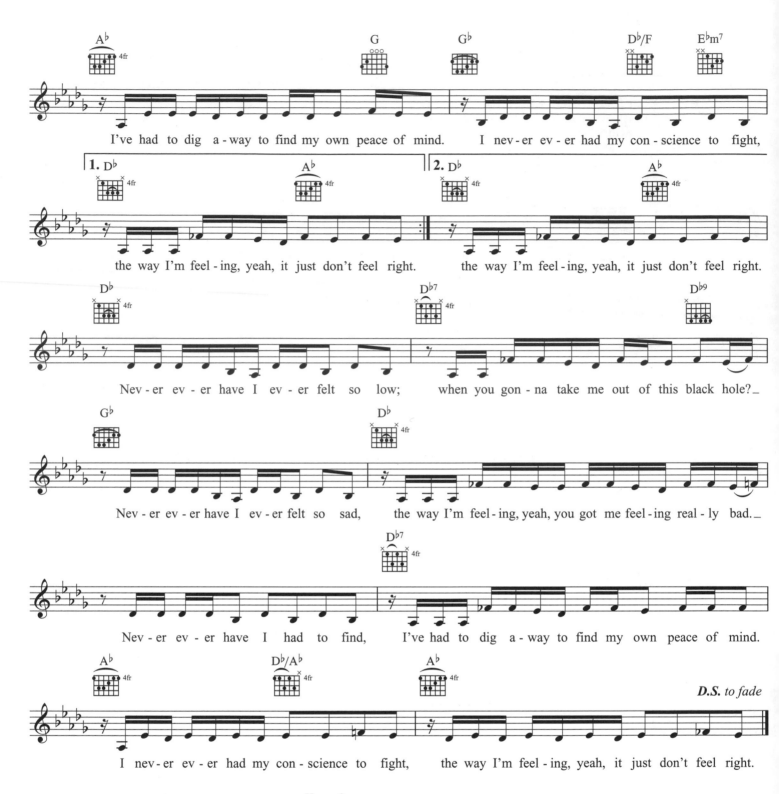

Verse 2:

I'll keep searching deep within my soul
For all the answers. Don't wanna hurt no more.
I need peace, got to feel at ease, need to be
Free from pain, goin' insane, my heart aches.

Sometimes vocabulary runs through my head
The alphabet runs right from A to Z.
Conversations, hesitations in my mind.
You got my conscience asking questions that I can't find.
I'm not crazy
I'm sure I ain't done nothing wrong.
Now I'm just waiting
'Cause I heard that this feeling won't last that long.

Ain't It Funny

Words & Music by Jennifer Lopez & Cory Rooney

1. It seemed to be like the per - fect thing for you and me.
2. Some - times I think that a true love can ne - ver be.

(* alternative key)

It's so i - ron - ic you're what I had pic - tured you to be.
I just be - lieve that some - how it was - n't meant for me.

But there are facts in our lives we can nev - er change.
Life can be cruel in a way that I can't ex - plain.

Just tell me that you un - der - stand and feel the same.
And I don't think that I could face it all a - gain.

Vocals Level 1 - Female

fun - ny how a mo - ment could just change your life,___ and you don't want to face what's wrong or right.___ Ain't it

strange how fate can play a part___ in the sto - ry of your heart.

sto - ry of your heart.

I locked a - way my heart, but you just set it free, e - mo - tions I felt

held me back from what my life should be. I pushed you far a - way and yet you stayed with

me, I guess this means___ that you and me___ were meant to be.___

D.S. repeat chorus ad lib. to fade

Ain't it

Constant Craving

Words & Music by K.D. Lang & Ben Mink

1. Ev - en through the dark - est phase, be it thick or
(Verse 2 see block lyric)
(* alternative key)

thin._____ Al - ways some - one march - es brave,

here be - neath my skin._____ And

con - stant crav - ing has al - ways_____

been. Crav - ing. Ah ha,_____ con - stant

crav - ing has al - - ways been, has

al - - - ways been. And con - stant crav -

- ing has al - ways____ been. Crav - ing, ah

ha,_____ con - stant crav - ing has al - - ways

Repeat to fade

been, has al - - ways been. Has

Verse 2:

Maybe a great magnet pulls
All souls towards the truth.
Or maybe it is life itself,
That feeds wisdom to its youth.

Out Of Reach

Words & Music by Gabrielle & Jonathan Shorten

Disc 1 Track 13/14

Vocals Level 1 - Female

16

Verse 3:

Catch myself from despair
I could drown if I stay here
Keeping busy every day
I know I will be O.K.
But I was so confused
My heart's bruised
Was I ever loved by you?

Out of reach *etc.*

Get The Party Started

Words & Music by Linda Perry

18

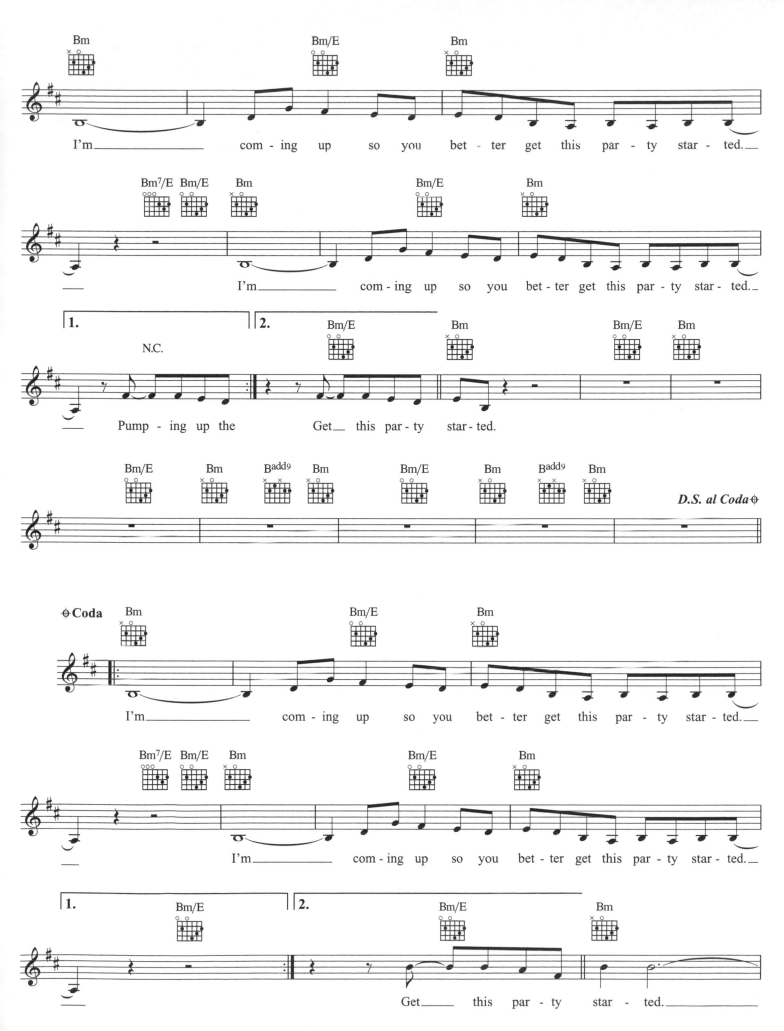

Verse 2:

Pumping up the volume, breaking down to the beat,
Cruising through the west side, we'll be checking the scene.
Boulevard is freaking as I'm coming up fast,
I'll be burning rubber you'll be kissing my Benz.
Pull up to the bumper, get out of the car,
License plates say stunning number one superstar.

I'm coming up *etc.*

Verse 3:

Making my connection as I enter the room,
Everybody's chilling as I set up the groove.
Pumping up the volume with this brand new beat,
Everybody's dancing and they're dancing for me.
I'm your operator, you can call any time,
I'll be your connection to the party line.

I'm coming up *etc.*

Grade 2 *Technical Exercises*

In this section, the examiner will ask you to perform the four exercises printed below. You do not need to memorise the exercises (and you may use the book in the exam) but the examiner will be looking for the speed and confidence of your response. The examiner will also give you credit for the level of your musicality.

Exercise 1: Rhythm Disc 1 Track 17

You will be asked to perform the exercise below as written to a backing track accompaniment in the exam. A short sound check will be given.

Exercise 2: Scales

You will be asked to perform a major, natural and harmonic minor scale in the following rhythms to a backing track accompaniment in the exam. You will be allowed to choose your own starting note between **A-E** which will be played to you before you begin. You will be asked a selection by the examiner and you will perform the exercise *legato* to a sound of your own choosing.

Major

Harmonic Minor

Exercise 3: Intervals

This exercise has two parts. (A) You will be asked to pitch a major or minor third or perfect fifth above notes **I**, **IV** and **V** of the chosen key in the above scale. The examiner will play the note for four beats on a CD and you will be asked to hold the note for four beats.

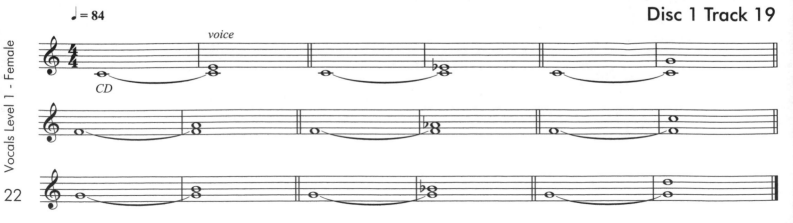

(B) You will be asked to pitch the root note of a perfect fifth chosen from the same notes. The examiner will play the interval for four beats on a CD and you will be asked to hold the note for four beats.

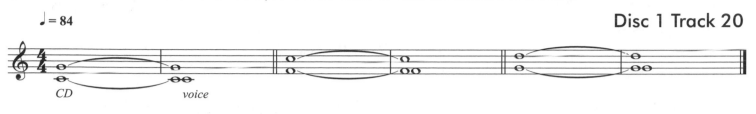

Disc 1 Track 20

Exercise 4: Phrasing & Dynamics

Disc 1 Track 21

You will be asked to prepare the following exercise. The examiner will play the backing on CD and you will be asked to sing the exercise, paying attention to the written phrasing and dynamics. You may perform the exercise using any sound that you consider appropriate.

Can't Get You Out Of My Head

Words & Music by Cathy Dennis & Rob Davis

♩ = 130

(La la la la___ la la la la la la la la___ la la la la.)

(La la la la___ la la la la la la la la___ la la la la.)
I just

can't get you out of my head. Boy your lov-ing is all I think a-bout. I just

can't get you out of my head. Boy, it's more that I dare to think a-bout.

1.

2, 3.

think a-bout. (2°) Ev-'ry night, e - ve - ry___ day.___
(3°) There's a dark se - cret in___ me.

To Coda ✛

Just to___ be there___ in___ your arms.___ Won't you___
Don't leave___ me locked in___ your heart. Set me

Killing Me Softly With His Song

Words by Norman Gimbel
Music by Charles Fox

(alternative key)*

1. I heard he sang a good song, I heard he had a style.

(Verses 2 & 3 see block lyric)

And so I came to see him and lis-ten for a while.

And there he was, this young boy, a stran-ger to my eyes.

Strum-ming my pain with his fin-gers, sing-ing my life with his words.

Kill-ing me soft-ly with his song, kill-ing me soft-ly with his song, tell-ing my whole life with his

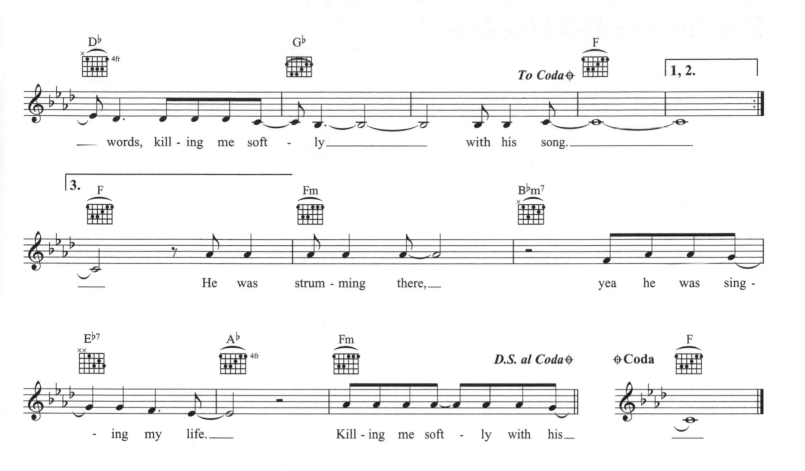

words, kill - ing me soft - ly _____ with his song. _____

He was strum - ming there, ___ yea he was sing -

- ing my life. ___ Kill - ing me soft - ly with his ___

Verse 2:

I felt all flushed with fever,
Embarrassed by the crowd.
I felt he found my letters
And read each one out loud.
I prayed that he would finish,
But he just kept right on.

Strumming my pain *etc.*

Verse 3:

He sang as if he knew me
In all my dark despair.
And then he looked right through me
As if I wasn't there.
But he was there this stranger,
Singing clear and strong.

Stumming my pain *etc.*

I'm Gonna Getcha Good!

Words & Music by Shania Twain
& Robert John "Mutt" Lange

Uh!

Let's go!

Don't

(* alternative key)

want you for the week - end, don't want you for a night. I'm

on - ly in - ter - est - ed if I can have you for life,___ yeah. 2. I

know I said I'm se - ri - ous,_____ and ba - by I am.

(Verse 3 see block lyric)

You're a fine piece of real es - tate, and I'm gon - na get me some land.

Oh,___ yeah. So don't try to run,_____ ho - ney,

Vocals Level 1 - Female

Verse 3:

I've already planned it
Here's how it's gonna be
I'm gonna love you
And you're gonna fall in love with me, yeah.

So don't try to run, *etc.*

Search For The Hero

Words & Music by
Mike Pickering & Paul Heard

search for the he - ro in - side your - self, un -

- til you find the key to your life._____

1. You've got to

2.

search in - side your - self.

N.C.

You've got to search.

Verse 2:

In this life, long and hard though it may seem,
Live it as you'd live a dream,
Aim so high.
Just keep the flame of truth burning bright.
The missing treasure you must find
Because you and only you alone
Can build a bridge across the stream.
Weave your spell in life's rich tapestry
Your passport to a feel supreme.

Waterloo

Words & Music by Benny Andersson,
Bjorn Ulvaeus & Stig Anderson

Vocals Level 1 - Female

Verse 2:

My, my, I tried to hold you back
But you were stronger, oh yeah
And now it seems my only chance
Is givin' up the fight.
And how could I ever refuse?
I feel like I win when I lose.

Waterloo *etc.*

The Tide Is High (Get The Feeling)

Words & Music by John Holt, Howard Barrett,
Tyrone Evans, Bill Padley & Jem Godfrey

Disc 2 Track 1/2

Vocals Level 1 - Female

Grade 3 *Technical Exercises*

In this section, the examiner will ask you to perform the four exercises printed below. You do not need to memorise the exercises (and you may use the book in the exam) but the examiner will be looking for the speed and confidence of your response. The examiner will also give you credit for the level of your musicality.

Exercise 1: Rhythm

Disc 2 Track 3

You will be asked to perform the exercise below as written to a backing track accompaniment in the exam. A short sound check will be given.

You will be asked to perform a major, natural minor, harmonic minor and major pentatonic scale in the following rhythms. You will be allowed to choose your own starting note from **A-E** which will be played to you before you begin. You will be asked a selection by the examiner and you will perform the exercise *legato* to a sound of your own choosing.

Major

Natural Minor

Harmonic Minor

Major Pentatonic

Exercise 3: Intervals

This exercise has two parts. (A) You will be asked to pitch a major or minor third, perfect fourth and perfect fifth by step above notes **I**, **IV** and **V** of the chosen key of the above scale. The examiner will play the note for four beats on a CD and you will be asked to sing as indicated.

Disc 2 Track 5

(B) You will be asked to pitch a major or minor third to root by step on the same notes. The examiner will play the interval for four beats on a CD and you will be asked to sing as indicated.

Disc 2 Track 6

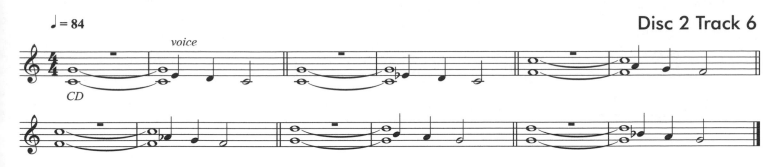

Exercise 4: Phrasing & Dynamics

Disc 2 Track 7

You will be asked to prepare the following exercise. The examiner will play the backing on CD and you will be asked to sing the exercise, paying attention to the written phrasing and dynamics. You may perform the exercise using any sound that you consider appropriate.

Mamma Mia

Words & Music by Benny Andersson,
Bjorn Ulvaeus & Stig Anderson

Vocals Level 1 - Female

Verse 2:

I've been angry and sad about things that you do.
I can't count all the times that I've told you we're through.
And when you go, when you slam the door
I think you know that you won't be away too long
You know that I'm not that strong.

Just one look *etc.*

Beautiful

Words & Music by Linda Perry

(Don't look at me) *Vocal ad lib.*

1. Ev -'ry day___ is so won - der - ful, then sud - den - ly it's hard to
2. To all your friends you're de - li - ri - ous, so con - sumed in all your

breathe. Now and then___ I get in - se - cure from all the
doom. Try - ing hard___ to fill the emp - ti - ness, the piec - es

pain, I'm so a - shamed. I am beau - ti - ful,___ no
gone, left the puz - zle un - done, is that the way it is? 'Cause you are beau - ti - ful,___ no
'Cause we are beau - ti - ful,___ no

mat - ter what___ they say.___ Words can't bring me___ down.
mat - ter what___ they say.___ Words can't bring you___ down.
mat - ter what___ they say.___ Yes words won't bring us___ down.

I am beau - ti - ful,___ in ev -'ry sin - gle way.___ Yes, words can't bring me___ down.___
You are beau - ti - ful,___ in ev -'ry sin - gle way.___ Yes, words can't bring you___ down.___
We are beau - ti - ful,___ in ev -'ry sin - gle way.___ Yes, words can't bring us___ down.___

Vocals Level 1 - Female

44

Hand In My Pocket

Words by Alanis Morissette
Music by Alanis Morissette & Glen Ballard

(* alternative key)

Complicated

Words & Music by Avril Lavigne, Lauren Christy,
David Alspach & Graeme Edwards

Better The Devil You Know

Words & Music by Mike Stock,
Matt Aitken & Pete Waterman

♩ = 124

Bet - ter the de - vil you know, bet - ter the de - vil you know.

(* alternative key)

Bet - ter the de - vil you know,

bet - ter the de - vil you know. Oh._____

1. 3. Say you__ won't leave me no more, I'll take you back a - gain.__
2. Our love was - n't per - fect I know, I think I know the score.__

No more__ ex - cu - ses____ no, no,____ 'cause I've heard____ them all be - fore,
You say__ you love me____ oh boy,____ I_____ can't ask for more,__

____ a hun - dred times__ or more._____ I'll__ for-
____ I'll come____ if you__ should call._____ }

What Can I Do

Words & Music by Andrea Corr,
Caroline Corr, Sharon Corr & Jim Corr

1. I have-n't slept__ at all__ in days,__

(Verses 2 & 3 see block lyric)

(alternative key)*

it's been so long__ since we__ have talked.__

And I have been__ here ma - ny times;_____

I just don't know__ what I'm do - in' wrong.__

1. What can I do__ to make__ you love__ me?

What can I do__ to make__ you care?____

What can I say__ to make__ you feel

Vocals Level 1 - Female

___ this? What can I do___ to get___ you there?_____

2. What can I do___ to make___ you love___ me?

What can I do___ to make___ you care?_____

What can I say___ to make___ you feel_____ this'?

What can I do___ to get___ you there?_____

No more wait - ing, no more ach - ing._____

D.S. al Coda

No more fight - ing, no more try - ing._____

⊕ Coda

What can I do___ to make___ you love___ me?

Verse 2:

There's only so much I can take
And I gotta let it go.
And, who knows, I might feel better, yeah
If I don't try and I don't hope.

Verse 3:

Maybe there's nothing more to say
And, in a funny way, I'm calm.
Because the power is not mine
I'm just gonna let it fly.

The Guru's Guide To Level 1 *Female Vocals*

Supplementary Material

Rockschool recommends the following songs in addition to the repertoire printed in this book. The list below shows the songs arranged by grade along with the publications in which they may be found.

Grade 1

Walking On Sunshine	*Be A Popstar: Holiday Hits*	IMP9053A
Heaven	*Audition Songs For Female Singers 11*	AM959156
Sing It Back	*Audition Songs For Professional Singers*	AM974578
It's My Party	*Sing & Party With Tear-jerkers*	IMP9803A
Lovefool	*Audition Songs For Professional Singers*	AM974578
Baby Love	*All Woman 4*	IMP9255A
Take My Breath Away	*All Woman 3*	IMP9187A

Grade 2

Holiday	*Be A Popstar: Holiday Hits*	IMP9053A
Genie In A Bottle	*Essential Audiotion Songs: Pop Divas*	IMP7769A
Beautiful Stranger	*Essential Audiotion Songs: Pop Divas*	IMP7769A
Thank You	*All Woman: Songbirds*	IMP9914A
I Only Want To Be With You	*All Woman 1*	IMP7077A
Almaz	*All Woman 3*	IMP9187A

Grade 3

Can't Fight The Moonlight	*Stars In Your Eyes: Number 1 Hits*	IMP9028A
Music	*Number 1 Hits*	IMP9028A
Oops! I Did It Again	*Sing With Britney*	AM974644
Stay With Me	*Sing & Party With Tear-jerkers*	IMP9803A
Fame	*Audition Songs For Female Singers 2*	AM950224
Crazy For You	*All Woman 3*	IMP9187A

Warm Up

It is important that you prepare for the exam by warming up your voice properly. You should ensure that you arrive at the exam centre within plenty of time to do this. We have arranged the elements of the grade exam such that the performances come at the end. The backing tracks and/or accompaniment are always variable in volume and you should always tell the examiner if you feel that you are straining to be heard.

Free Choice Pieces

In grade exams you are allowed to perform one song not specified in this book or the companion Level 1 *Male Vocals* book. This maybe a hit from the chart or a song composed by yourself. In performance certificate exams you are allowed to perform up to two songs not specified in this book.

If you wish to find out whether a free choice piece song is appropriate for the grade, you may either contact Rockschool and submit the song for adjudication, or look on our website www.rockschool.co.uk and consult the free choice piece criteria.

Marking Schemes

The tables below show the marking schemes for grade exams and performance certificates. All Rockschool exams are marked out of 100 and the pass mark for a grade exam is 65% and for a performance certificate is 70%.

Grade Exam

Element	Pass	Merit	Distinction
Technical Exercises	11 out of 15	12 out of 15	13 out of 15
General Musicianship Questions	3 out of 5	4 out of 5	5 out of 5
Aural Tests	6 out of 10	7 out of 10	8 out of 10
Piece 1	13 out of 20	15 out of 20	17 out of 20
Piece 2	13 out of 20	15 out of 20	17 out of 20
Piece 3	13 out of 20	15 out of 20	17 out of 20
Unaccompanied Piece	6 out of 10	7 out of 10	7 out of 10

Performance Certificate

Element	Pass	Merit	Distinction
Piece 1	14 out of 20	16 out of 20	18 out of 20
Piece 2	14 out of 20	16 out of 20	18 out of 20
Piece 3	14 out of 20	16 out of 20	18 out of 20
Piece 4	14 out of 20	16 out of 20	18 out of 20
Piece 5	14 out of 20	16 out of 20	18 out of 20

Examination Criteria

Rockschool examiners assess all examinations according to strict guidelines. Copies of these for vocals can be found on the website www.rockschool.co.uk or direct from our offices. Please ring **020 8332 6303** for further details.

Exam Regulations

Entering a Rockschool exam is easy. Please read through the instructions on the back of the entry form accompanying this book carefully, before filling it in. Information on current fees can be obtained by ringing Rockschool on **020 8332 6303** or by logging on to the website www.rockschool.co.uk.

1/06(57229)